The Wondrous Adventures Of A Medieval Shrew

Story & Illustrations by Alan Raymond

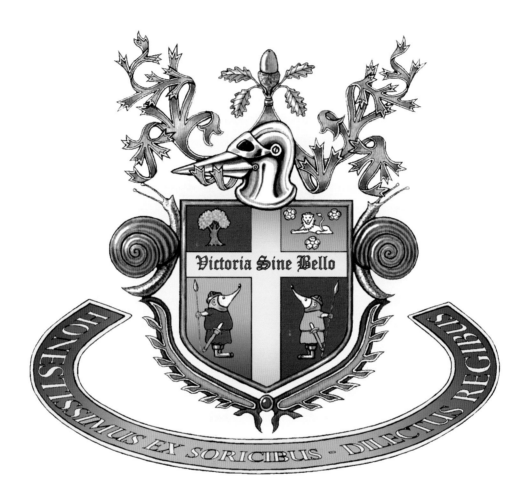

First Published In Great Britain in 2000
by Alan Raymond Publications Ltd
Cypla
Llanbedr
Gwynedd, LL45 2ND N.Wales.

ISBN 0-9539147-0-4

Printed and bound in Great Britain by Gomer Press, Llandysul, Ceredigion, Cymru

Around Ludlow castle in 1282
There lived wild boar and badgers and foxes and mice,
But this is the tale of brave Silas the shrew,
Silas Sorrocks to be quite precise.

Not including his parents, Grizelda and Seth,
Young Silas was one of a family of eight;
There was Silas himself, Ben, Jemima and Beth,
Sefton, Bruno, Matilda and Kate

They all lived in a hole between two big stone blocks
Underneath a high tower in the old castle wall
Which ringed Ludlow Hill like a great crown of rocks
Standing more than four hundred shrews tall

The Sorrocks's home was kept warm all the year
By a great Norman oven in the room overhead;
While Grizelda fried snails and old Seth brewed his beer,
The king's cooks just above them baked bread.

So shrews went for a drink or a swim or a bath
At the clear river Teme, where the alders grew tall
And most of the shrews used the same Roman path –
(Old Shrewdinium Way, I recall)

Life had mostly been quiet for Ludlovian shrews
Till the king fought Llywelyn, the famous Welsh prince,
After that the king's troops (so said all of the news)
Had remained in the town ever since.

Only water was scarce in the old castle grounds
For the well was much deeper than Mortimer's tower –
If you tossed in a stone and then waited for sounds
You could stand there a whole shrew half-hour!

Not that shrews had much trouble with Edward the First,
In fact, most days the king wasn't even in town;
No, the trouble was started by Jasper the Worst,
A bad weasel from Wooferton Down.

Jasper Dunk, (his real name) had left home in disgrace
After causing a riot in Tinker's Hill copse
With his mates, Snotty Sam, Spotty Jake and Ratface,
Winklepicker, Gutbucket and Wopse.

Now a troublesome weasel most country folk hate,
And these seven rough rodents were shunned more than many,
So they wandered the hills from Bringewood to Cock Gate
Seeking homes, but they couldn't find any.

But when Jasper the Worst spotted Ludlow ahead,
Grim and ghostly and grey at the onset of night,
He persuaded his friends (who were quite easily led)
That the time was upon them to fight.

'I'm right sick of this wanderin'' he said with a sigh,
"I wants me an 'ome on the old castle 'ill.
If kings can go fightin' fer land, so can I –
I can an' I blinkin' well will!'

'But there's millions of shrews own that 'ill an' the vale,'
Said Wopse, 'They outnumber us fifty t' three!'
'Then we'll get us a gang an' wear suits of chain mail!'
Jasper said with a cackle of glee.

'What's good fer a king is as good fer us too –
We can get us an army down Overton way –
We'll creep up on the valley an' bash every shrew
If it takes us all night an' all day!'

So the weasels went southward to Overton Hall
To a weaselsmith known as Blackhammer the Third,
Who with Snout, his assistant, made suits for them all
While his messengers sent out the word.

Of course, this was unknown to the shrews in the vale,
Who, some folk might have said, lived in ignorant bliss;
Making worm pies and snail soup and Real Shrewletts Ale,
Unaware there was something amiss.

Very soon wicked weasels from woods all around
Came to join Jasper's army, from Wootton and Whitton,
From The Riddle, The Goggin and Old Yarpole Pound,
Basket's Gate, Stanton Lacy and Snitton.

So it was that in August in 1282
Jasper Dunk's weasel army marched north a whole day
And proceeded to bash every unprepared shrew
Who set foot on Shrewdinium Way.

Now of all a shrew's features his nose is the best,
Or his snozzle, as shrews would prefer it be called,
But it gets where he's going before all the rest
So in fights it gets terribly mauled.

The weasels that day took the vale by surprise
And snozzle-bashed shrews every place they were found,
While Silas's family looked on with sad eyes
Hardly daring to make any sound.

That night Jasper's army camped out on the slope
And at sundown the shrews heard him give a great shout –
'Pack yer things up an' move – you aint got any 'ope!
You got just one week left t'get out!'

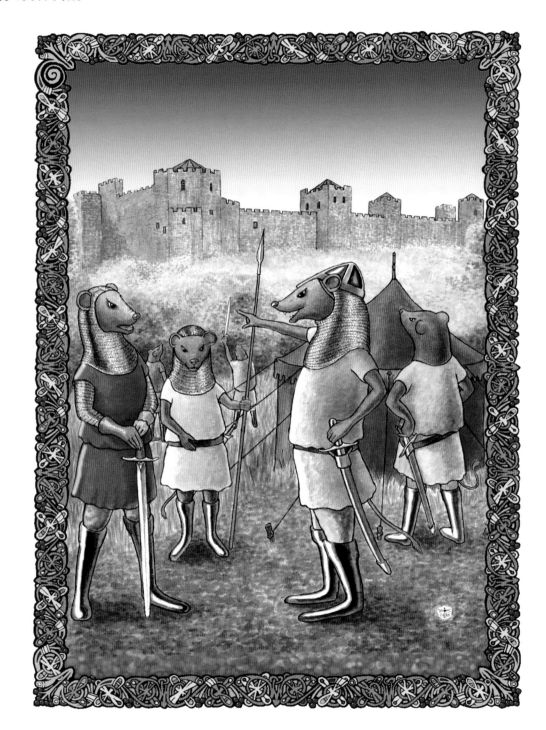

Silas turned to his father – 'What do we do now?
We can't give up the valley to Jasper the Worst!'
'No, you're right,' mumbled Seth, 'We must beat him – but how?
We must think about what to do first.'

An idea buzzed around in young Silas's head,
A plan he would have to try out on his own,
So at midnight he quietly snook from his bed
And crept out on the hillside alone.

'We've some chain mail and helmets packed up in a chest
That my grandfather's friends used in 1264,
But there's only enough for eighteen shrews at best –
We'll have to get hold of some more.'

With just a big stick carried under his arm,
He silently tip-toed to Jasper Dunk's camp,
And before the watch-weasel could sound the alarm
Silas bashed him and put out his lamp.

Then he bashed two more weasels asleep near a tree
And a fourth one on guard at the head of the vale,
Until soon he had silenced a full thirty-three
And collected their helmets and mail.

But Silas was seen as he made his way back
By Gutbucket and Wopse, who were lying in wait,
And who gave his poor snozzle a terrible whack
As he ran past the old castle gate.

They left him flat out in the grass, wet with dew,
Where he woke with the dawn feeling tired and sick,
And he found they had taken their chain-mail back too
With the helmets and even his stick.

Near the castle gate road Silas sat on a stone
As the weasels cheered Jasper just over the rise,
And feeling defeated, worn-out and alone,
Wiped the tears away from his eyes.

'It's useless!' he thought, with a shrug and a sigh,
'All the chain mail in Shrewdom will have no effect!
And you don't need to look very far to see why –
It's our snozzles we need to protect!'

In a full suit of mail and a cloak of flame red
And with sparkling gold spurs curling out from each heel,
He wore bright silver gauntlets, and perched on his head
Was a great heavy helmet of steel.

Just then, from the gatehouse there came a great cry,
The drawbridge was raised and the gate opened wide,
And Silas drew back as a horseman raced by
With a banner raised high at his side.

Silas gasped as the soldier flew down Ludlow Hill
Leaving clouds of red dust in the air where he'd been,
And he watched till he turned at the bridge by the mill
But could barely believe what he'd seen.

'That's it!' exclaimed Silas, 'That's the answer for sure!
A snozzle protector and a suit made of tin!
What a fool I was not to have seen it before –
With something like that we could win!'

Silas ran up the hill like a shrew gone berserk
And arriving at home shook his father awake,
'I've a plan Dad!' he yelled, 'And I'm sure it will work –
But we've lots of tin helmets to make!'

So Seth listened as Silas explained his idea,
And spoke of the helmeted soldier in red,
While the whole Sorrocks family sat around him to hear
On the edge of the big double bed.

'It's a bosting idea young Silas my boy –
The best! Just the best!' Seth concluded at last,
And I know just the shrewsmith we ought to employ,
We must do him some drawings – and fast!'

Of all the fine shrewsmiths from Wootton to Greete,
Old Tarragon Bagot was quickest and best
And in only five days the tin suits were complete
And returned to Seth's house in a chest.

So with Silas's drawings Seth crept off, unseen,
Down to Tarragon Bagot of Steventon Wood,
Who with his assistants was terribly keen
To rid Ludlow of Jasper for good.

Then by moonlight some messengers sent out the news,
Through Linney and Dinham to Ludford Bridge Mill,
That Seth Sorrocks had need of the bravest of shrews
To meet near his house on the hill.

So it was that two hundred shrews gathered about
In the shadows, not far from the Hanging Tower wall
And while Seth gave the plan, Silas handed suits out
To the biggest and strongest of all.

Then quiet as ghosts through the grass tall and damp,
They descended the hill in the dead of the night
And formed a great circle around Jasper's camp
Where they waited until it grew light.

When the weasels awoke, all the shrews were amazed
To see Silas walk into their camp on his own,
With his suit of tin clanking and his bashing stick raised,
Calling Jasper to come out alone.

Unable to see the shrew army nearby
Wopse decided that Silas was daft in the head,
But as he drew near with his stick held up high
Silas turned around and bashed him instead.

In a circle, the weasels were ready to spring,
But were arguing just who should bash the shrew first,
Then the whole camp fell silent as into the ring
Dressed in chain mail, came Jasper the Worst.

"A shrew in a can? – what a comical sight!
Why you look proper daft, that's a fact!' Jasper said.
"Am I right in supposin' you're plannin' t'fight
With that stupid tin box on yer 'ead?'

'We'll fight a duel,' Silas said after a pause,
"And if I should win I'll forbid you to stay –
But if I should lose, then this valley is yours –
Every shrew will depart here today!'

'Well well, me good mates – did you 'ear the young fool?'
Jasper said with a smirk to the whole weasel crowd,
'This 'ere dustbin on legs wants to fight in a duel!'
And the weasels all laughed out aloud.

Then just as the shrew was about to reply,
A rumble of thunder rang out through the trees
And both weasels and shrews gazed up into the sky
But there wasn't a cloud on the breeze.

Then a pale, dusty mist rose up over the vale
And the thunder grew strong in the ground all around,
Till at last, moving fast on the riverside trail
There appeared the cause of the sound.

On brightly clad warhorses fifty shrews tall
There came three hundred soldiers with spears and swords,
And high in his saddle at the head of them all
Rode the king, with his dukes, earls and lords.

On a crimson-clad charger with eyes flashing white,
His bright scarlet surcoat bearing lions of gold,
The tall, blonde-haired king was as fearsome a sight
As a weasel or shrew could behold.

Jasper's gang lost their courage and wanted to fly,
But Silas was struck by a sudden idea;
He ran down the hill with his sword held up high
Then bowed down as the army drew near.

Then he shouted out loud as he jumped in the air
'Silas shrew at your service!' – again and again,
Till at last the king looked down and noticed him there
And signalled a halt to his men.

Said the king, climbing down from his warhorse, 'Good grief!
Weasels in chain mail and armour on shrews?
Why the sight is amazing beyond all belief!
Just wait till the queen hears the news!'

Silas bowed very low and again called his name,
'Yes, I heard!' Edward said, 'And there's no need to shout!
I can't see why you've stopped me young shrew – all the same
You'd best tell me what this is about.

'Forgive me your Highness,' said one of the knights,
'But should we give time to a weasel or shrew?
Let them sort out their own silly problems and fights –
There are better things for us to do!'

'I'd like you to settle an argument sir,
- a serious argument,' Silas replied.
'You can hear both our stories and then I'd prefer
To allow your Royal Highness decide.

'Excuse me,' said Silas, addressing the lord,
'I'm not talking to you, as you very well know!
Interrupt me once more and I'll take out my sword
And chop off the end of your toe!'

'Calm down master Silas,' said the king with a sigh,
'It's true that I have many more things to do,
So perhaps you should give me just one reason why
I should stand here and listen to you?'

'I won't argue with that,' said the king with a grin,
Then stroking his beard, he frowned at the shrew,
'But why are you wearing a suit made of tin?
And just what do you want me to do?'

'Whose is this land?' said the shrew to the king,
'Why this land's mine of course!' said the king to the shrew.
'Then we shrews should consult you on every such thing!
We're your subjects too – isn't that true?'

Just then, Seth shuffled forward and gave a great bow,
'If it please your Royal Highness,' he said, 'I must tell,
That it wasn't us shrews sir who started this row,
As all these here weasels know well.

Sir Silas Sorrocks

'We shrews sir, have lived in these parts many a day,
Since the emperor Shrewvius came to this land,
And he it was built this Shrewdinium Way
Right where you and your soldiers now stand!'

'So he gets him an army and leads an attack
And we had to decide pretty quick what to do,
So we made our own armour and came here to fight back,
And that sir, is when we saw you.'

All our ancestors came here ten centuries ago,
And ever since then most folk left us alone,
Now this Jasper Dunk comes here and tells us to go,
'Cause he wants Ludlow vale for his own!'

Said the king to the weasels, who stood near the trees,
'Jasper Dunk, I request you to come over here –
And the rest of you kindly draw near if you please,
I would like everybody to hear.'

Sir Silas Sorrocks

With his head hung down low, Jasper walked to the king
Feeling more and more nervous each step of the way,
While the armies both gathered close by in a ring
Wondering just what King Edward would say.

'But I'll let master Silas decide what to do,
As you've given his family and friends such offence,
Though before he gives sentence I have to ask you
If you'd like to speak in your defence?'

'I usually chop heads off for crimes such as these!'
Said the king to the weasel, who trembled with fear,
'Or lock them in dungeons and lose all the keys –
Or put them in stocks for a year!'

Jasper stared at his boots and gave a great sigh,
'I'm sorry your 'ighness,' he said, 'It's no use'
And he sniffed as he wiped a big tear from his eye.
'I can't think up no proper excuse.'

'S'just that me an' me mates got no place of our own,
An' we gets tired o'travellin day after day,
Wherever we tries t'stay folks always moan,
An' everyone sends us away!'

The king gazed at Jasper and then at the shrew,
'I suppose I should banish the weasels?' he said,
'But you master Silas must choose what to do –
'Should we put them in prison instead?'

'I'm right sorry we treated these shrews 'ere so rough,
An' I promise we won't never do it no more.
They can 'ave all our sticks an' our spears an' stuff,
An' the chain mail what all of us wore.'

But the shrew had a different idea in his mind,
Now poor Jasper was looking so terribly sad.
'Prison,' thought Silas, 'Is rather unkind –
The weasel's not really that bad.'

'There's some land up at Deepwood, three miles to the west,'
Silas said, 'Near the forest – the weasels know where,
And if they behave sir, I'd like to suggest
Jasper Dunk and his friends could live there.'

Then everyone threw down their sticks and their spears,
Silas bowed to the king, Jasper bowed to the shrew,
Then all of the weasels gave Silas three cheers,
And the shrews cheered the king three times too.

'Well I'm blowed master Silas! – I have to admit,'
Said the king, 'This all sounds quite peculiar to me!
And I'm not sure these weasels deserve it one bit!
But if that's what you want, I'll agree.'

The king gazed down at Jasper and then scratched his head,
'I still think you need teaching a lesson – but then,
I have never gone back on a promise,' he said,
'So now you and your friends are free men!'

'Free weasels you mean!' chuckled Silas politely,
'Precisely!' said Edward, who turned slightly red,
'But remember, I won't let you off quite so lightly
If there's any more trouble,' he said.

'Well with luck,' said the king, 'You'll all be safe and sound
So I must join my soldiers and bid you goodbye.'
But then Silas's helmet, which lay on the ground
Glinted brightly and caught the king's eye.

Jasper gave a low bow and shook Silas's paw
And he promised that he and his friends would be good,
Then after he'd bowed to King Edward once more
He went off on his way to Deepwood.

Edward knelt on the ground for a closer inspection,
'What a marvellous idea!' he said, 'Yes indeed!
Why in this I could breathe well and still have protection!
It's exactly the shape that I need!'

'It's a snozzle protector,' said Silas, 'That's all!'
'But it's just what I'm looking for!' Edward replied.
'Don't you think,' Silas asked, 'That it's rather too small –
And your Highness's head is too wide?'

'If I tried to wear yours I would look such a fool!'
Edward laughed, 'But I could have one made to my size,
With a point at the front so I'd stay nice and cool,
And a twiddly bit for my eyes!'

Then said Edward, 'It's really a clever design,
Will you grant me permission to use your invention?'
Said Silas, 'Your Highness, the pleasure is mine –
Whatever may be your intention.'

'Then tonight,' said the king, 'In my banqueting hall
We shall have a great feast in your honour my friend,
So please pass on the word to your family and all –
I invite everyone to attend!'

Well, the scene at the castle that night was amazing
With the lords and their ladies all beautifully dressed,
While along all the walls yellow torches were blazing
And trumpets announced every guest.

The king and his court danced in stately formation
To the sound of a crumhorn and sackbut quartet,
While the shrews bowed and curtsied and used the occasion
To dance a genteel minuet.

Some danced regal quadrilles or a slow hedgehog trot,
While others waltzed around with bright bows in their hair,
And some chose a shrew-step or stately gavotte
While the young shrews just leapt in the air.

Then, when the guests had all danced fit to fall
The trumpets rang out and the dance floor was cleared,
The king clapped his hands, and there in the hall,
A brightly dressed servant appeared.

He carried a carpet of scarlet and gold
With some tiny carved steps and a small wooden stage,
And when the red carpet was fully unrolled
The king took his sword from the page.

'I'm so glad you could come,' said the king with delight,
'I'm pleased that so many were free to attend,
For we're all gathered here to honour tonight,
My new-found, but rather small friend!'

The shrews gazed at each other with questioning eyes
And looked all around for the mystery guest,
But the king, with a grin, took them all by surprise
As he bowed and made one last request.

Then at last the whole court began talking aloud
And the shrews laughed and danced and shook everyone's hand,
Then they carried poor Silas the length of the crowd
And placed him down next to the stand.

'Would the brave Silas Sorrocks come forward awhile?'
Edward said, bowing low and extending his hand,
But poor Silas went woozy and smiled an odd smile
And was almost too nervous to stand.

Edward gave him a sword and a red velvet gown,
Then read out from a scroll hung with tassels of blue,
'I do hereby declare Silas shrew of this town
A most wise and remarkable shrew!'

Silas knelt on the stage and then very politely
Gave thanks to the king for the comments he'd made,
But the king touched both Silas's shoulders quite lightly
With the tip of his sword's silver blade.

'I name you Sir Silas!' he said, 'And I'm happy
To have as my good friend the first knighted shrew,
A brave local hero and all-round good chappie
And inventor of twiddly bits too!'

At this the whole crowd gave a thunderous applause
Then drank Silas's health with the finest French wine,
While a bell rang and servants drew back two great doors
And bid everyone enter to dine.

When the feasting had ended, the dancing went on
Till the wee hours of morning, when stars lit the sky,
For the truth is that everyone there had such fun
No-one noticed the time passing by.

On the tabletops patterned with gold-embossed leather
There were small chairs and tables set out rear to rear,
So the shrews and the courtiers could all sit together
And share in the food and good cheer.

And that's how Silas Sorrocks became a shrew knight
At the court of King Edward in 1282,
By solving his problems with no need to fight
And inventing some twiddly bits too.

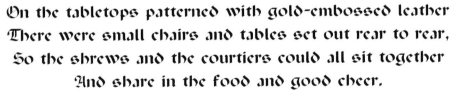

And from that time the vale has known peace all its days
For the weasels behaved themselves down in Deepwood,
And Jasper the Worst had so altered his ways
He became known as Jasper the Good.

And finally Silas gave up independence
For a pretty young shrew maid named Flissity Quayle
And some of his great great grandshrewlet descendants
Still dwell to this day in the vale.

And he married a fair weasel maiden from Clun
Who was (so said all of the rumours) delectable,
And raised three weaslet daughters and one weaslet son
Who (it's said) grew up very respectable.

And the shrew's fame lives on in a place of renown,
Once a hamlet named Shrew's Borough, so called by the queen
Which is now known as Shrewsbury, the old border town
Where today very few shrews are seen.

But from Ludford to Dinham and on down the vale
Near the castle which these days no kings or queens use,
Shrewfolk still tell their shrewlets the wonderful tale
Of brave Silas, most honoured of shrews.

For there's many a story of Silas's quest
To save forests and visit strange lands far away
But for now we'll stop here for a long, well-earned rest
And save those tales for some other day.

THE END

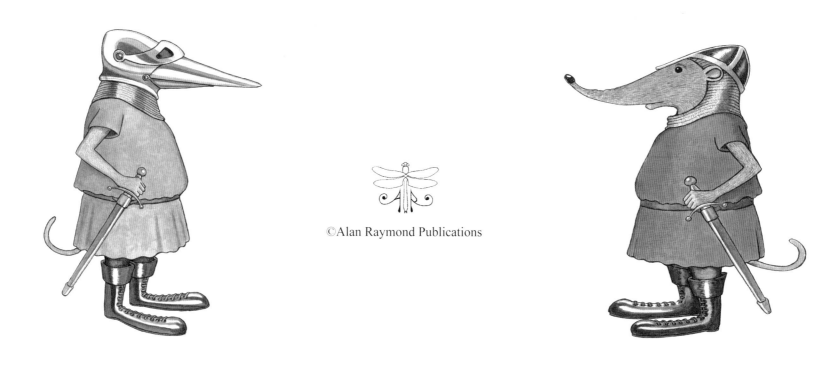

Look out for the Silas Web Page, on www.sorrocks.com